FOREWORD ∞

Industrial heritage relating to the textile-finishing industry has been the poor relation of cotton spinning, even though it was such a significant part of the textile-manufacturing economy in the Greater Manchester area. Its buildings, which are generally very functional, are seen as less architecturally pleasing than the iconic cotton mills that once dominated Greater Manchester's skyline. This is reflected in the designation of heritage assets, with around 95 mills being listed as regionally or nationally important, but only one finishing works. Equally, archaeological recording has focused more on the historic buildings of cotton manufacturing, as well as the below-ground remains of their power systems. However, using the planning system, community engagement and specialist research skills of industrial-period experts, it has been possible to start redressing the balance by targeting the sites of print, dye and bleach works for desk-based and archaeological building surveys and excavations. The results are already showing the worth of this approach. Whilst most textile-finishing works have been destroyed, it is clear that many former sites still retain very significant and extensive below-ground remains relating to processing and power systems. This booklet enables the reader to understand and enjoy some of the remarkable discoveries made by archaeologists in recent years, focusing on the historic printing industry in Bury district.

CONTENTS

Spreading the word about Greater Manchester's fascinating but relatively unrecognised archaeology is challenging. One of the ways to do this is through publication in the form of 'popular' booklets. I have considerable pleasure therefore in introducing you to this publication, which is Volume 6 in a new series covering the wonderful archaeology of the whole of the Greater Manchester area: Bolton, Bury, Manchester, Oldham, Rochdale, Salford, Stockport, Tameside, Trafford and Wigan. This new series is called 'Greater Manchester's Past Revealed', and provides a format for publishing significant archaeology from developer-funded, research or community projects in an attractive, easy to read, and well-illustrated style.

NORMAN REDHEAD, County Archaeologist, Greater Manchester

·1·

During the nineteenth century, Lancashire rose to prominence as an international centre for the production of cotton goods. The huge cotton-spinning mills that still punctuate the skyline of many towns in the North West provide testament to the textile industry's impact on the economic and social development of the region. However, cotton spinning was only one branch of the industry, and to a large extent its initial growth in Lancashire during the late eighteenth century was based on the achievements of the area's established calico-printing trade. This fulfilled a crucial role in producing high-quality cotton goods, although its legacy in the modern landscape is perhaps not as well represented as other branches of the industry.

Calico printing is a term applied generically to the printing of coloured designs onto any sort of textile fabric, although it originated to describe specifically the printing of cotton cloth. Introduced into England in the 1670s, the calico-printing trade gravitated to Lancashire during the eighteenth century, where it developed from the domain of skilled craftsmen to a true factory based process. Purpose-built print works were established initially in the Preston and

An eighteenth-century block printer

Blackburn areas, where the application of ground-breaking technological innovations was pioneered. By the early nineteenth century, print works had been set up in other parts of the county, with important groups developing around Stockport, and along the River Irwell and its tributaries to the north of Manchester. Many works expanded to incorporate dedicated bleaching and dyeing departments, providing a cloth-finishing service to the textile trade.

The demise of the English cotton industry in the mid-twentieth century led to the closure of most of the region's print works, many of which have since been demolished, as the buildings could not be adapted easily to alternative uses. However, the buried remains of these factories frequently survive, and have increasingly been the focus of archaeological investigations, providing an insight into the development of this fascinating industry.

Aerial view of the easement for the West East Link Main pipeline, near Golborne in 2010 (© United Utilities)

An important opportunity to examine the remains of a nineteenth-century print works arose from a proposal by United Utilities to lay a major new water pipeline across the North West. The West East Link Main, as it is known, takes a 55km route between Liverpool and Bury. Hailed as the biggest project of its kind ever undertaken by an English water company, the pipeline crosses three motorways, five railway lines, numerous major roads, canals, rivers, and large areas of abandoned mine workings.

Installing the pipeline necessitated the excavation of a wide easement along the entire route, although its precise course was not finalised until a range of environmental factors had been considered and preliminary investigations undertaken. These considerations included the potential for the construction programme to damage buried archaeological remains. In some places, however, the scope to adjust its line was limited by the natural topography, as in Springwater Park in the Whitefield area of Bury, where the route was constrained by the steeply sloping valley side and the River Irwell. This area had been dominated in the nineteenth century by Springwater Print Works, which was built in 1827 and remained in use as a textile-finishing works until the 1938-9.

The footprint of the works could therefore not be avoided by the pipeline, and its construction would inevitably result in the loss of any buried remains that could potentially yield important evidence for the historical development of the site. Consequently, the Greater Manchester Archaeological Unit (GMAU), which provides advice to Bury Council, recommended that an archaeological investigation of the site was undertaken in advance of the construction programme. This was carried out by Oxford Archaeology North (OA North) in 2010-11, and involved the excavation of a 5m-wide trench across the site of the print works.

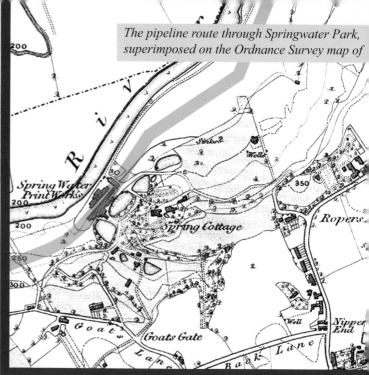

The remains of the Adelphi Dye Works, on the eastern bank of the River Irwell in Salford, excavated by OA North in 2008

As with most modern archaeological fieldwork, the excavation was undertaken by professional archaeologists working in a construction-site environment. Similar work on former textile-finishing sites completed recently in Greater Manchester include the comprehensive survey and excavation of the Wallsuches Bleach Works in Horwich, undertaken by the University of Manchester Archaeological Unit (UMAU). Driven by the redevelopment of the site for housing, this important study was carried out in several stages between 2000 and 2009, and provided new information on the early origins and character of textile finishing. The redevelopment of the Adelphi Dye Works in Salford for new housing was similarly accompanied by an archaeological excavation in 2008, which provided a rare insight into the layout of an early nineteenth-century dye works. More recently, in 2010, Northamptonshire Archaeology carried out an excavation at Bury Ground, the site of the first print works in Bury.

Commercial archaeology is not the only means by which textile-finishing sites have been excavated, however, and several very successful investigations of former print works have been undertaken by local volunteers working under the supervision of professional archaeologists and the guidance of GMAU. One such project, carried out in 2009, involved volunteers from the Bolton Archaeological Society and the local community who, under the direction of staff from OA North, excavated part of Tootill Print Works in the Breightmet area of Bolton. A larger community based project in 2011 targeted the site of Tottington Print Works in the Kirklees Valley, near Bury. Initiated by Bury Council, in consultation with GMAU, this project involved a survey of the extensive standing fragments of the works, coupled with the clearance and excavation of key parts of the site.

The exciting and important discoveries from these archaeological investigations of print works are presented in this booklet, which also summarises the deveopment and progress of this key branch of the textile industry. The sites examined all lay within the River Irwell catchment area, in the heart of the calico-printing district, and whilst the projects had similar research objectives, the results were achieved via very different means.

THE RIVER IRWELL CATCHMENT

The River Irwell catchment covers more than 700 square kilometres, incorporating most of the modern county of Greater Manchester and part of Rossendale in Lancashire, an area which includes the moors of the South Pennines. The main rivers are the Irwell, Roch, Croal, Medlock and Irk, which all flow via the Irwell into the Manchester Ship Canal.

These rivers and their tributaries cumulatively drain the urbanised districts of Manchester, Salford, Bury, Bolton, Oldham and Rochdale. They also provided the foci for the calico-printing industry from the early 1800s. The growth of this industry, with its increasing demand for a constant supply of water, led to the modification of numerous watercourses, with many kilometres of walled banks, culverts and weirs. Notable legacies of this industrialisation are the numerous reservoirs, some of which have become havens for wildlife and recreation.

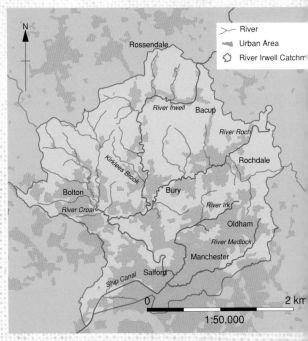

The extent of the River Irwell catchment

Two major concentrations of print works had become established in the River Irwell catchment by the middle of the nineteenth century. The first group lined the banks of the Irwell, Medlock and Irk as they flowed through the urbanised periphery of Manchester and Salford. The second group was centred on Bury, and included the large factory at Bury Ground, several in the Irwell and Kirklees valleys to the north, and a chain of works along the Roch and Irwell rivers to the south.

Island Lodge at Tottington, near Bury, was expanded from a small mill pond in the 1820s to supply Tottington Print Works with water

Print works required a riverside location for several reasons, but primarily to obtain the huge volumes of water that were needed for washing the cloth as it was passed through the various stages of the printing process. The amount of water used was calculated in 1868 by a Parliamentary Commission on river pollution, which studied a sample of large print works and concluded that each establishment consumed an average of 400,000,000 gallons *per annum*. A similar volume of liquid effluent was discharged from the works, and a riverside location offered considerable advantages for ease of its disposal, although the resultant pollution caused problems. The printing process depended on clean water, and the pollution led many works to supplement their supply by pumping fresh water from wells, or building reservoirs to capture ground run-off. The widespread adoption of filter beds at print works in the late nineteenth century helped to reduce the pollution of the rivers.

Water also provided the print works with a valuable source of motive power, particularly during the eighteenth century, when the driving of machinery was dependent upon waterwheels. Even after the widespread adoption of steam power in most industries, some print works continued to employ waterwheels; Bury Ground Print Works, for instance, was still powered entirely by waterwheels in the 1840s.

The distribution of print works in mid-nineteenth-century Lancashire

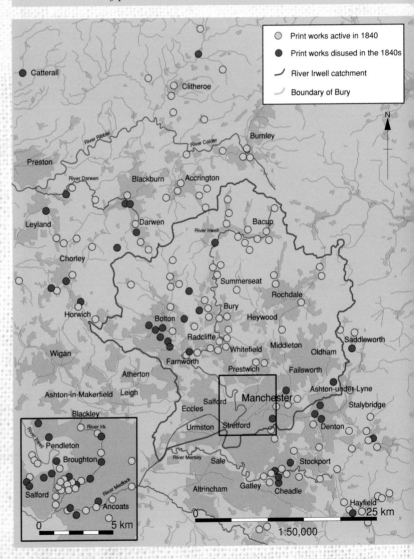

Legend:
○ Print works active in 1840
● Print works disused in the 1840s
╱ River Irwell catchment
╱ Boundary of Bury

The origins of the English calico-printing industry can be traced to the seventeenth century, when a type of fine cotton cloth known as chintz began to be imported from India. Noted for its exotic and brightly coloured patterns, Indian chintz quickly became very fashionable. Copies began to be produced by English printers, with the first recorded print works being established on the banks of the River Thames near Richmond in 1676. The success of this enterprise heralded a rapid expansion of the trade. This was centred firmly on London, the main point of supply for imported calico.

Printing was the domain of highly skilled craftsmen, who earned a reputation as a distinct class of artisans. One observer described 'the rather curious costumes' worn by London printers in the mid-eighteenth century, noting their 'cocked hats, scarlet coats and top boots, and in other respects being very aristocratic in their way'.

The popularity of chintz alarmed the established woollen manufacturers, who lobbied parliament successfully for legislation to protect their trade; the use of Indian chintz was prohibited by law in 1701, whilst a further Act of Parliament in 1721 banned the use of all printed, painted or dyed calicos.

A fine example of eighteenth-century chintz

However, printers soon found ways of copying chintz using fustian, which was exempt from the new laws as it was a mixed fabric. Fustian was made by the Lancashire weavers, and the Act of 1721 undoubtedly stimulated a significant increase in its production. The advantages of a local supply of cloth, coupled with ample supplies of fresh water, the cheapness of land for bleach crofts, and the lower level of wages, led to a shift of the calico-printing industry from London to Lancashire.

The first print works in Lancashire, set up by Messrs Clayton of Bamber Bridge near Preston, was in production by 1764. This was hugely successful, and more print works were soon established, with an important group on the River Darwen near Blackburn, where the locally produced fabric, known as 'Blackburn grey', proved especially suitable for printing. Another pioneering works was established by Robert Peel, a yeoman farmer who began printing cotton in *c* 1764 at Brookside Mill in Oswaldtwistle. Peel discovered that a roller with a decoration carved in relief could be used to print a repeat pattern onto cloth. Combining wooden rollers and engraved copper cylinders on a machine, Peel was the first to carry out mechanised calico printing on an industrial scale. The first pattern he produced was based on a parsley-leaf design, hence he later became known as 'Parsley Peel'.

The Peel family became one of the most famous names in Lancashire's early cotton industry, being responsible for introducing several important innovations in handloom weaving, mule spinning and power-loom weaving. They are also accredited with founding the cotton industry in Bury, when they began calico printing at Bury Ground in 1773, the first proper industrial factory in the upper Irwell Valley. Brooksbottom Mill at Summerseat was also established as a print works in the same year.

In 1774, the regulations against printed calicos were repealed, enabling printers to produce their own chintz from pure cotton. This quickly became more popular than the imported material, and acted as a major impetus to an expansion of the cotton industry in Lancashire.

An early view of Brooksbottom Mill, looking southwards along the Irwell Valley towards Bury. Built as a calico-printing factory in 1783, the Peel family had expanded and converted the site for cotton spinning by the early 1800s

Block Printing

The oldest method of printing calico relied on skilled craftsmen using hand-printing blocks. These carefully engraved blocks were made of layers of wood sandwiched together, one side of which had a raised printing surface that varied depending on the type of cloth and the pattern to be printed. Three types of block were commonly used: line blocks for printing outlines and small details; blotch blocks with felted surfaces for large areas of colour; and ground blocks for small areas of colour. Each colour was applied with a different block, and there could be over a 100 blocks in a set.

A wooden printing block

A large print works would employ several hundred block printers, each having their own table. This consisted of a heavy flagstone placed on a wooden or iron framework. A woollen blanket, stretched tightly over the flagstone, provided the surface upon which to print the cloth. At one end of the table, a series of guide rollers extending to the ceiling allowed the newly printed goods to be suspended and dried.

It was common practice for a child, known as a tierer, to assist the block printer in his work. The tierer's main duties were to push a tub of printing colour along the table, and to clean the blocks. The work did not require much physical exertion, although it was very monotonous and frequently involved long hours. A Parliamentary Commission set up in 1842 to examine the working conditions for children at print works found the average working day to be 12 hours long, and heard reports of children falling asleep at their tubs.

An early nineteenth-century engraving of a block printer and tierer at work

Machine Printing

Whilst capable of producing intricate results, block printing by hand was a slow process. Cutting fine details onto the wooden blocks was also difficult and, once in use, these wore down quickly. These problems were addressed by Thomas Bell, who began printing cloth with engraved copper plates in 1770. This worked in the reverse manner to hand blocks; the engraved lines were the printing area, and the smooth surface of the plate was kept clear of colour. Whilst this technique met with some success, great difficulty was experienced in making the printed impressions join up exactly, and the technique was thus confined to simple patterns.

In 1783, Bell patented a roller-printing machine that revolutionised the industry. His original patent was for a machine fitted with six engraved copper rollers that was capable of printing six colours, building up the final multi-coloured design as the cloth passed each roller in sequence. Whilst this was not achieved initially, Bell nevertheless demonstrated the method to be practical by the printing of one colour with perfectly satisfactory results. The difficulty he had encountered was to keep the six rollers, each carrying a portion of the pattern, in perfect register with each other. This defect was soon overcome by Adam Parkinson of Manchester and, in 1785, Bell's machine with Parkinson's improvement was used successfully for printing calico in multiple colours by Messrs Livesey, Hargreaves, Hall & Co at Mosney Print Works in Walton-le-Dale, near Preston.

Detail engraved on a copper roller used for textile printing

A printing machine comprised a cast-iron pressure cylinder that was mounted in vertical slots attached to a rigid iron framework, allowing it to slide up and down. The cylinder was wrapped with lapping, which enabled the roller to force the cloth to be printed into the lines of the engraving. The engraved copper roller was mounted in fixed bearings beneath the pressure cylinder, and was supplied with the printing colour by a wooden roller that revolved in a colour box below. A key component was the 'doctor', a sharp blade of steel that rested on the engraved roller and scraped off surplus colour to leave only that in the engraved lines. Multi-colour machines had several rollers, each carrying part of the pattern and fitted with its own colour trough and doctor knife.

The mechanised calico-printing process in the 1830s, showing, on the left, a machine with engraved copper rollers transferring the pattern onto the cloth, whilst on the right is a block printer adding fine detail using a hand block

The roller-printing machines were each tended by three hands. The machine printer stood in front of the machine to ensure that the impression made by the roller was perfect. A young person called a 'back-tenter', usually aged between 15 and 18, stood at the back of the machine and had to ensure that the cloth passed between the rollers evenly and was free of any creases. The third hand was a 'plaiter-down', frequently a boy aged between 11 and 15, who had to lay the printed cloth in folds as it returned after passing through the padding stoves, where the pieces were dried.

The introduction of machines increased the output of printed calico considerably, although hand-block methods continued to be used for applying intricate detail to machine-printed cloth until the middle of the nineteenth century. Documents dating from the 1840s show that most print works in Lancashire also housed numerous tables for hand-block work in addition to printing machines.

A Maturing Industry

Technological advances led to the widespread adoption of printing machines from the 1860s, with a corresponding reduction in hand-block work. However, the art of block printing enjoyed a renaissance in the 1870s, largely due to the powerful influence of William Morris. Widely acclaimed as one of the most influential pattern designers of the nineteenth century, Morris was determined to revive traditions of craftsmanship that he considered to have been lost as a result of industrialisation. His printing business was successful, but the revival of the trade was restricted largely to niche markets.

Hand-block printers at work at Merton Abbey Print Works in East London, re-opened by William Morris in 1881

Morris' active interests in calico printing coincided with an era of peak prosperity for the textile-printing industry. However, the trade entered a decade of depression in the late 1880s, largely as a result of inefficiency, price cutting and long credit; some 25 printing firms went out of business in just three years after 1888. The solution to these problems, which also beset other branches of the textile industry, was amalgamation.

Between 1897 and 1899, the majority of printing firms were grouped into three associations, of which the largest was the Calico Printers' Association (CPA). This was a merger of 46 printing firms, together with 13 merchanting concerns, representing 85% of British textile-printing capacity. The Association's principal objective was to reduce competition and costs, which it achieved by centralising the procurement of raw materials and by concentrating production. It also provided financial investment to modernise many of its print works, although the closure of some of the older and less efficient sites was an inevitable consequence. By 1918, the number of print works operated by the Association had fallen to 29, with a further reduction to just 11 by 1939.

ESSENTIAL PREPARATION: THE DEVELOPMENT OF BLEACHING AND DYEING

In order for cotton cloth to be printed or dyed successfully, it had to be freed from any impurities by bleaching, which rendered the cloth completely white. The traditional method of bleaching involved a lengthy process that could take several months to complete. The first stage, known as 'bucking', was to boil the cloth in alkaline lye made from wood ashes, followed by a thorough washing in water and steeping in buttermilk. Whitening was then achieved by spreading the cloth out in the open air, and exposing it to the sun for long periods.

A nineteenth-century engraving of a traditional open-air bleach croft

The equipment used by eighteenth-century bleachers was very simple, consisting of a large vat known as a 'kier' that was used for bucking, and troughs of stone or wood for washing and steeping. The other essential requirements were an abundant supply of fresh water, and sufficient land available to spread the cloth out. This latter requirement provided a commercial use for the infertile moorland that characterised tracts of Lancashire.

The traditional bleaching process captured on a nineteenth-century lithograph

Factory Based Bleaching

It was becoming increasingly clear by the late eighteenth century that a more efficient means of bleaching cloth was needed to keep pace with the major improvements in other branches of the textile industry. A significant breakthrough was achieved in 1798 by Charles Tennant, who introduced a bleaching powder made by impregnating dry-slaked lime with chlorine gas. Another crucial development was the introduction of mechanisation; water and steam power began to be used to drive machines, including dash wheels and washing machines, squeezers, mangles and calendars. These innovations, together with an exponential growth in the demand for cotton goods, led to the widespread adoption of the factory system, with the transferral of the bleaching process indoors. During the nineteenth century, many print works developed their own bleaching departments, thus providing a complete cloth-finishing service.

Once delivered to a print works, the first step was to create a perfectly smooth surface on the 'grey' cloth by removing any fine fibres and frayed filaments derived from weaving. This was achieved in the singe house, where the cloth was passed over red-hot plates. It was then transferred to the bleach croft for the 'grey wash'. During this process, the cloth was impregnated with souring liquor to break down oils and grease, washed, and squeezed dry through rollers.

In the early nineteenth century, the individual bundles of cloth were washed in dash wheels, which were large cylinders divided into compartments. These were largely superseded by a machine invented in 1828 by David Bentley that could wash lengths of cloth sewn together into a continuous rope.

Dash wheels at the Dukinfield bleach works of Thomas Hoyle & Sons in 1843

The scouring action of the washing machine removed some of the impurities from the cloth, but would not destroy the fine waxy coating on the fibres entirely. This was achieved by boiling the cloth in a kier, which involved circulating the lime solution continuously through the cloth at a temperature of at least 100°C for several hours. Once completed, the cloth was washed thoroughly to remove all the lime solution.

The next stage was the 'grey sour', which involved treating the cloth with a weak solution of hydrochloric acid to dissolve any vestiges of lime and other insoluble soaps. It was then washed thoroughly to discharge all the dissolved matter, prior to being transferred to another kier for boiling in soda ash. After another thorough washing, the cloth was then ready for actual bleaching, or chemicing, which was achieved by saturating the cloth in a clear solution of chloride of lime, or bleaching powder.

After allowing the chemical reactions to take place, the last step was to pass the cloth through a dilute solution of sulphuric acid, a stage known as the 'white sour'. This was followed immediately by a final washing in clean water, which rendered the cloth perfectly pure. It was then passed through a pair of specially padded squeezing rollers, and thence into either centrifugal driers or a range of drying cylinders. Once it had been dried, the cloth was stored in 'white pile' cisterns ready for printing.

Some figured fabrics, especially those woven in checks and stripes, required careful stretching and straightening on a machine known as a 'stenter' before they could be printed. Finally, the cloth was wound onto rolls of convenient size for mounting on the printing machines.

Schematic section through a bleach croft

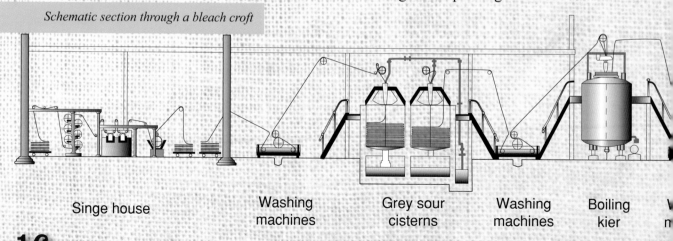

Singe house   Washing   Grey sour   Washing   Boiling
                     machines   cisterns   machines   kier

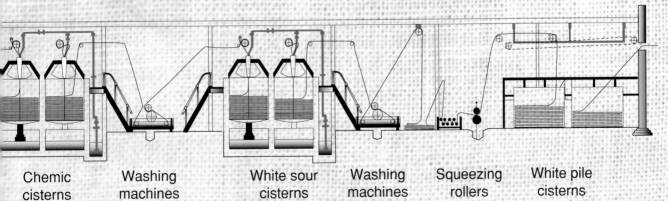

| Chemic cisterns | Washing machines | White sour cisterns | Washing machines | Squeezing rollers | White pile cisterns |

The Dyes

Whilst bleaching was an essential initial stage in the printing process, the quality of the finish was also dependent upon the dyes. The two agents required for dyeing are the colouring matter and a mordant, which 'fixes' the dye in the cloth. Traditionally, the principal mordant used for dyeing was alum imported from the Papal States in Europe, where it occurred naturally as the sulphate mineral alunite. However, in the seventeenth century, a means of manufacturing alum chemically from certain types of shale was discovered, leading to the birth of an important new industry. This was largely confined to north-east Yorkshire, where the Jurassic shale strata contained the aluminium salts and pyrites required to produce alum.

The dyes used in the textile industry until the nineteenth century were derived mostly from plants. The main sources were indigo, madder and logwood, although cochineal insects and tropical sea snails were also used. Some natural colouring matter, however, could not be made into dyes easily, or did not adhere to the cloth well. These problems were solved by the introduction of chemically produced dyes, which cost less and offered a huge range of new colours.

The first synthetic dye was discovered by accident in 1856 by William Henry Perkins. Perkins found that a rich purple dye could be produced by reacting aniline with potassium dichromate, and then extracting the dye by adding alcohol. He set up his own company to produce 'mauve aniline', heralding the birth of a new industry that was to be of great benefit to the dyeing and printing trades. By 1859, synthetic dye was the height of fashion, with Queen Victoria wearing a mauve dress to the International Exhibition of 1862.

At the age of 18, WH Perkins invented the first synthetic dye whilst conducting experiments at the Royal College of Chemistry in search of a cure for malaria

A nineteenth-century lithograph of the dyeing process

Chemical engineering expanded the range of techniques available for applying dyes to the cloth. A popular method was to print mordants such as aluminium or iron acetates onto the cloth prior to applying the dye, which would only adhere to the printed area. An alternative technique, known as resist dyeing, involved printing wax or a similar substance onto the fabric. It was then immersed in dye, which would not adhere to the waxed areas, leaving plain patterns on the coloured fabric. In 1802, Robert Peel revolutionised this process by introducing a means of printing a pattern in wax using mechanical rollers. The same effect was achieved by printing a bleaching agent onto previously dyed fabric to remove the colour, a method known as discharge printing.

Whilst the management of the colouring process required much skill, the machinery used by nineteenth-century dyers simply comprised a large cistern, or beck, over which was mounted a roller. A long rope of cloth was wound onto the roller in loose loops, and then rotated in and out of the beck filled with hot water and the required dye. Once the cloth had been dyed, it was washed and soaped to remove unwanted colourants.

The origins of the factory based cotton industry in the Irwell Valley around Bury can be traced to 1773, the year in which the famous partnership of Howarth, Peel & Yates purchased a ruined corn mill at Bury Ground, and redeveloped the site as a print works. This soon became one of the largest and most successful works in England, acclaimed for 'the novelty of the styles, designs and beauty in colouring' of its cloth.

The extent of this important works in the mid-nineteenth century is shown on historical maps, which depict an array of buildings. Their arrangement typifies the layout of a print works of this period, which were described in 1842 to be 'generally very irregularly built, without regard to symmetry of architecture. They seem to be a succession of after-thoughts…'

The Ordnance Survey map of 1847, showing the layout of Bury Ground Print Works, and the area excavated in 2010

Printing at Bury Ground ceased in 1866, when the works was given over entirely to bleaching. It finally closed in the 1960s, when many of the buildings were demolished. Part of the site was cleared for a new development in 2010, providing the opportunity for an archaeological investigation.

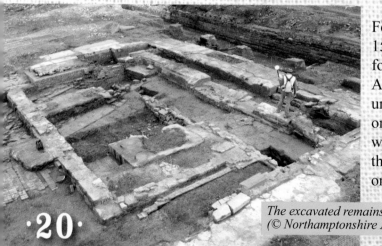

Following initial evaluation trenching, some 1500 square metres of the site were selected for detailed excavation by Northamptonshire Archaeology. The oldest remains to be unearthed included the stone foundations for one of the original buildings. The foundations were cut by a substantial stone wall, seemingly the remains of the 'Machine Room' marked on historical mapping.

The excavated remains of the 'Machine Room', built in c 1820 (© Northamptonshire Archaeology)

Whilst few interior features survived, the name given to this room suggests that it had contained the printing machines. Evidence for further expansion of the print works was provided by the remains of the 'New Machine Room', which had been added onto the existing Machine Room by the early 1830s. Excavation revealed a huge stone-lined trough, measuring some 17m long and 1m wide. This may have formed a common sump beneath a row of dash wheels, used for washing the cloth.

Building on their success at Bury Ground, Peel, Yates & Co set up another print works on the River Irwell in *c* 1784, choosing a site in the small village of Ramsbottom, to the north of Bury. This works was taken over in 1806 by the Grant brothers, who played a key role in the growth of Ramsbottom as a textile-manufacturing centre. Other important print works that were set up in the locale during this period included those at Stubbins and Rose Bank, situated to the north of Ramsbottom, and Kirklees Print Works, which was established on the Kirklees Brook near Tottington in 1791.

Stone-lined trough in the 'New Machine Room' at Bury Ground (© Northamptonshire Archaeology)

One of the earliest print works to the south of Bury was Hampson's Mill, a small woollen factory that was converted for printing in *c* 1781. The mill lay on the west bank of the River Roch, at its confluence with the Hollins Brook. This minor watercourse was also exploited for industrial purposes, when a print works was erected at Hollins Vale, approximately 700m to the east of Hampson's Mill, in 1801. Some two years later, another print works was set up on the River Roch at Blackford Bridge, a mere 500m downstream of Hampson's Mill.

Another important early print works to the south of Bury was founded at Radcliffe, on the River Irwell. This had originated as a smallware factory, but was adapted for printing by Shaw, Docker & Yates in the late eighteenth century. Part of this site was subject to an archaeological evaluation by OA North in 2005, although it seemed to have been largely destroyed during the construction of the East Lancashire Paper Mill that occupied the site subsequently.

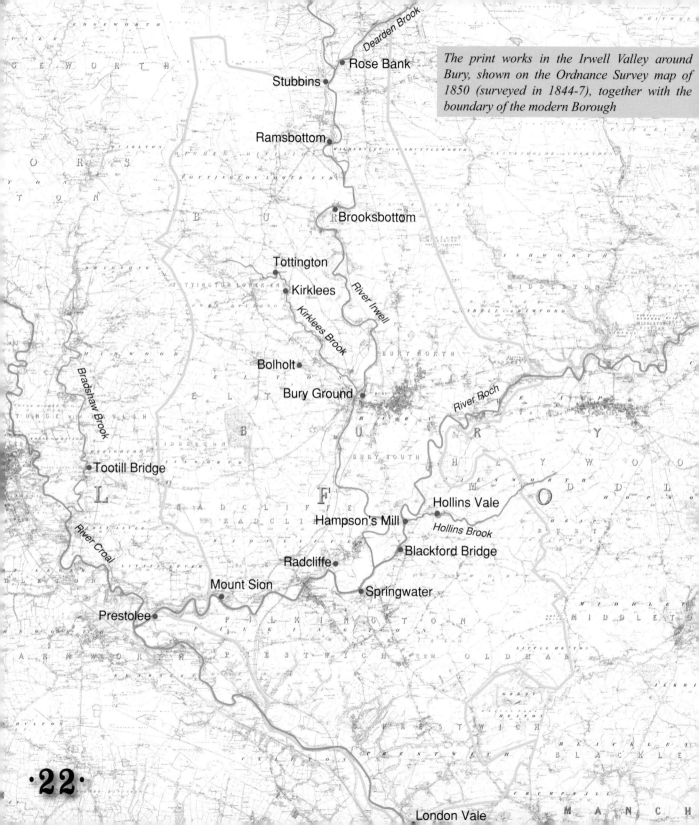

Dearden Brook

Rose Bank

Stubbins

Ramsbottom

Brooksbottom

Tottington

Kirklees

River Irwell

Kirklees Brook

Bolholt

Bury Ground

River Roch

Bradshaw Brook

Tootill Bridge

Hollins Vale

Hampson's Mill

Hollins Brook

River Croal

Blackford Bridge

Radcliffe

Mount Sion

Springwater

Prestolee

London Vale

The remains of a water-powered pump at Mount Sion Print Works, surveyed by the Manchester Region Industrial Archaeology Society in 2010, leading to its designation as a Grade II listed building

Another wave of print works was established during the 1820s. Amongst those to the north of Bury town centre was Tottington Print Works, a former water-powered cotton mill in the Kirklees Valley that was converted for printing in 1820. In the same year, Bolholt Bleach Works near Walshaw was expanded to include capacity for textile printing and, in 1821, the Grant brothers replaced their old printing shop in Ramsbottom with the Square Works, which was reputed to be the most progressive and modern print works in Europe. Several works were also set up along the River Irwell to the south of Bury during this period, including those at Springwater and Mount Sion.

The large print works at Mount Sion was built in 1828. By 1840, the works boasted six printing machines and a total of 170 tables for hand-block printing; Bury Ground was the only works in the area to contain more machines and printing tables at that date. However, it was remodelled as a bleach works in 1859, and was largely rebuilt after a devastating fire in 1913, although a water-powered pump that formed part of the original print works survives *in-situ*. This pumped effluent discharged from the works to a reservoir, from where it was fed through a sand filter to enable the water to be reused.

The increased output of printed calico that resulted from the addition of these new works placed the Irwell Valley at the forefront of the English textile-printing industry by the middle of the nineteenth century. At the heart of this area was Bury.

THE WEST EAST LINK MAIN IN THE IRWELL VALLEY

An important chance to assess the remains of nineteenth-century print works in the River Irwell catchment arose from the construction of the West East Link Main pipeline between Prescot Reservoir near Liverpool and Woodgate Hill Reservoir in Bury. In 2008, as part of the preliminary works carried out for this major scheme, United Utilities commissioned an archaeological study of the pipeline corridor. This involved desk-based research of the available historical material, coupled with a walk-over survey of the entire 55km course of the pipeline. This work aimed to identify any sites of archaeological interest that lay along the proposed route that would be vulnerable to damage or destruction as part of the construction programme.

In the light of the archaeological study, it proved possible in some instances to alter the final course of the pipeline to avoid impinging on historic remains. In those cases where the scope to revise the route was limited by other considerations, a record of any archaeological remains was made either before or during the construction work.

Aerial view of the Irwell Valley, showing the route of the new water pipeline

Blackford Bridge

The proposed route of the pipeline to the south of Bury included a 2km section between Whitefield and Radcliffe, following the course of the rivers Roch and Irwell. This section crossed the sites of former print works at Blackford Bridge and in Springwater Park.

Blackford Bridge Print Works lay on the eastern bank on the River Roch, close to its confluence with the Irwell. Printing commenced there on a small scale in c 1803, although the works expanded during the 1820s to become a large concern, with five printing machines and 100 tables for hand-block work in use by the early 1840s. The works came under the control of the Calico Printers' Association in 1900, but was transferred to the Eagle Dyeing Company ten years later, signalling the end of textile printing at Blackford Bridge.

The overgrown remains of Blackford Bridge Print Works

Stone-built tanks surviving at Blackford Bridge

Whilst the buildings were largely demolished in the 1970s, surviving fragments of the works were recorded during the archaeological walk-over survey. These included the foundations of several buildings, a weir across the river and the remains of the associated water-management system, and five large, stone-built tanks that may have been used as dye becks. These remains were all left *in-situ*, as the route of the pipeline was altered to avoid the site.

Springwater Print Works

Less than 1km south-westwards from Blackford Bridge, the route of the pipeline crossed the site of Springwater Print Works, situated on the southern bank of the River Irwell. There, altering the route was not a viable option, and it was thus necessary to excavate the pipe trench through the print works.

Springwater Print Works was established by Alfred Thomas in 1827, forming one of a group of purpose-built printing factories set up in the Irwell Valley to the south-west of Bury during the late 1820-30s. A census of English

Installing the West East Link Main in Springwater Park

print works compiled in 1840 accredits Springwater with 129 tables for hand-block printing, but only two machines, implying that most of the output was generated by hand-block printers, who produced cloth 'mostly for the home trade'. During busy periods in the early 1840s, Alfred Thomas employed up to 200 block printers, and more than 120 children under the age of 13, producing some 60-70,000 pieces of printed cloth annually. The works manager at that time was James Lord, who had worked previously at Bury Ground Print Works.

Alfred Thomas was declared insolvent in 1844, and after a short period of closure, the print works was taken over by the London-based firm of Felkin & Innes. However, this firm ceased trading in 1852, and the works was advertised for sale by auction in April 1853. Amongst the items of equipment included in the auction were 108 engraved copper rollers, more than 3000 printing blocks, and 'the valuable contents of the laboratory'.

A plan of Springwater Print Works, drawn in 1834

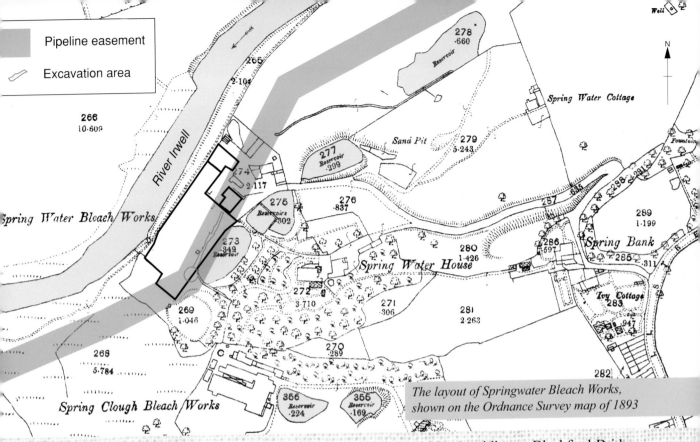

The layout of Springwater Bleach Works, shown on the Ordnance Survey map of 1893

The works was taken over by William Chambers, a 'cotton bleacher' residing at Blackford Bridge. Within a few years, William Chambers had passed the business on to his sons, Richard and Andrew, giving rise to the firm of R&A Chambers. Production at Springwater was moved over entirely to bleaching, and the original buildings were remodelled into a single processing range.

The 1890s proved to be a difficult decade for all branches of the textile industry, and numerous established firms ceased trading. In 1900, some 60 bleaching firms, including R & A Chambers, amalgamated into the newly formed Bleachers' Association Ltd. This resulted in some financial investment in Springwater Works, with a bank of three new Lancashire boilers being purchased to supply the steam required by the bleaching plant, which included more than 20 steam engines. Further modernisation included the installation of electrically powered machinery in 1908, representing a relatively early application of this new type of power in a textile-manufacturing site.

R&A Chambers ceased trading in 1938-9, marking the end of bleaching at Springwater Works. The buildings remained in use for storage purposes until the early 1970s, when the site was cleared and landscaped as a country park.

Excavating the remains of the print works, showing the reservoir wall to the rear

In 2010-11, a 5m-wide trench was excavated along the route of the pipeline as it crossed the site, allowing a section of several adjoining parts of the works to be examined. Well-preserved structural remains of various buildings were exposed, representing different stages in the development of the works.

The earliest remains were revealed at the southern end of the trench, and included a substantial wall that had been built using carefully worked stone blocks, with a solid core of mortared stone rubble. This had undoubtedly formed a section of one of the five reservoirs built to serve the print works. A second stone wall, set at a right-angle to the reservoir, may have been part of a conduit that channelled water to the print works. Some of the reservoirs were supplied from the River Irwell, whilst others captured clean water from ground run-off, which was also pumped from the underlying natural gravels via a 60ft (18.3m) deep well.

Excavation a short distance to the north exposed the foundations of a wall that was more than 1m wide. Built of hand-made bricks set in a lime-based mortar, typical of early nineteenth-century construction, this large wall had probably been part of one of the print works' buildings. It was parallel to a substantial structure that was composed of worked blocks of sandstone, and housed four vertical iron rods, indicative of its use as a foundation bed for a steam engine.

Remains of the foundations for the chimney, with the excavated engine bed to the rear

More remains of the works' steam-power plant were revealed a short distance to the north of the engine bed and included the foundations for a square, brick-built chimney that was more than 2.3m wide. The base of the associated flue leading from the boiler house was also exposed, and similarly comprised hand-made bricks.

These remains of the steam plant may have been built for the print works, supplying power to the dash wheels and other machinery, although they certainly continued in use following the conversion of the site to a bleach works in the 1850s. The chimney is marked on a plan of the site drawn for the Bleachers' Association in 1906, whilst the excavated engine bed lay in a part of the bleach works (Room 10) listed as an 'engine area, materials store and loading bay' in an accompanying schedule.

The steam-power plant for the print works had been supplemented by a waterwheel. This evidently remained in use after the site was converted to a bleach works, as a waterwheel, 36ft (10.97m) in diameter, with wooden arms and sheet-iron buckets, is itemised in a schedule of the works dating from 1867.

Plan of Springwater Bleach Works drawn in 1906 (National Trust, Quarry Bank Mill Archive)

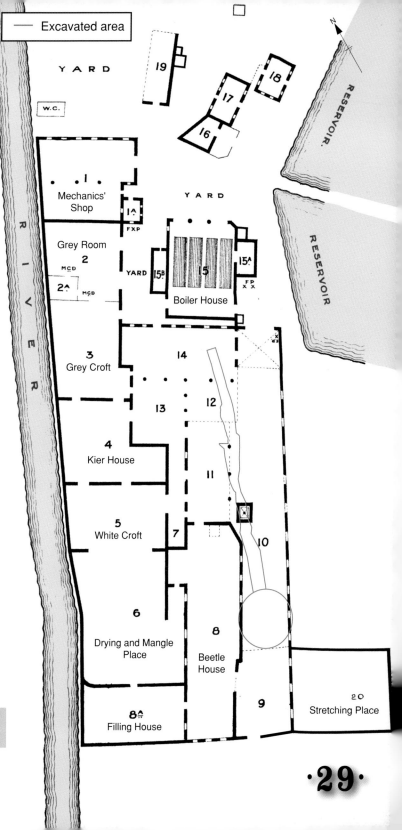

Machine beds exposed in the 'calendar and mangle place'

A brick-built wall, the position of which corresponded to the eastern wall of the 'calendar and mangle place' (Room 11), was excavated to the north of the chimney. A series of stone blocks set into the floor represented the foundation beds for the machinery in this room, which will have been mainly mangles and calendars.

Similar remains were revealed in the adjacent 'calendar and mangle place' (Room 12), although the housing for a late nineteenth-century steam engine was also discovered. This largely comprised a concrete setting, which had been partly decorated with black and white tiles arranged in a recurring diamond pattern. A large iron pipe set within the housing will have delivered steam to the engine from the boilers, which lay beyond the northern end of the excavated trench.

The excavated housing for a late nineteenth-century steam engine

The machines housed in Room 12 were similar to those in Room 11, being dominated by backfilling mangles and calendars. These were designed to restore and improve the finished appearance of the cloth, which was often rendered limp and harsh to the touch by the bleaching process. The machines were powered by a series of small steam engines, until the installation of electric motors in the early twentieth century.

A backfilling mangle by Whitehead & Poole (Manchester) Ltd

Excavation of the northern end of the trench unearthed a concrete surface, which will have formed the internal floor of the third 'calendar and mangle place' (Room 14). Dating to the late nineteenth or early twentieth century, the floor contained numerous settings for machinery.

The floor had collapsed in places, revealing a network of drains. These were all composed of machine-made bricks, and were probably built at the same date as the overlying concrete floor, representing a reconstruction of this part of the works.

Network of drains exposed beneath the floor of Room 14

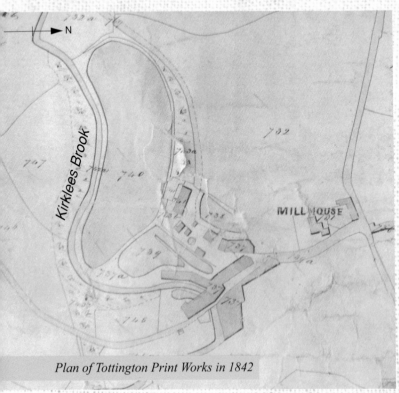

Plan of Tottington Print Works in 1842

The site of another nineteenth-century print works that was investigated in 2011 lies astride the Kirklees Brook near Tottington, some 7km to the north of Springwater Park. Flowing into the River Irwell at Bury Ground, the Kirklees Brook has a long history of use by water-powered industry; documents dating back to 1296 mention a corn mill on the brook at Tottington. This was still at work in 1790, when a cotton mill was added to the site, forming one of several water-powered spinning mills that were set up on the Kirklees Brook during the late eighteenth century. Other early textile factories included the Kirklees Print Works of 1791 and the associated Kirklees Bleach Works, which was built between 1794 and 1803.

The cotton mill was advertised for sale in 1819, by which date cotton-spinning factories in remote rural settings like the Kirklees Valley were proving to be uneconomical when compared to their new steam-powered counterparts in Lancashire's growing urban centres. The ample supply of clean water provided by the Kirklees Brook, however, made the site an ideal location for a textile-printing works. Recognising this potential, Joshua Knowles purchased the mill in 1820 and converted it for use as a print works, which necessitated adding several new buildings and reservoirs to the site.

Samuel Knowles, step-brother of Joshua

Joshua Knowles had begun his career in Ramsbottom, where he served an apprenticeship to the Grant brothers. This evidently provided Knowles with a good grounding in the art of calico printing, enabling him to develop his own successful business at Tottington from 1820. In 1836, he took on as an apprentice his 15-year-old step-brother, Samuel Knowles, who proved to be very talented. Samuel is noted for introducing a ground-breaking system of using chlorate of potash to oxidise and precipitate colours used for printing, which 'did much to enhance the reputation of the firm'.

Following the death of Joshua Knowles in September 1853, Samuel leased the works from Joshua's widow, and took over the business. The lease contained a list of the machinery in the works, which included eight printing machines, each powered by their own small steam engine. One of the machines, capable of printing 12 colours, represented the most advanced printing technology that was available.

Samuel expanded the works considerably during the 1860s and 1870s. He was also instrumental in promoting the Bury and Tottington District Railway Company, which provided Tottington with a rail link to Bury and Manchester by

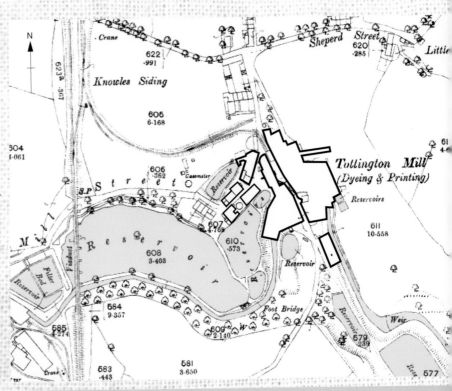

The extent of Tottington Print Works, shown on the Ordnance Survey map of 1893

opening a line to Holcombe Brook in 1882. The line was connected by a private siding that led directly to the print works, allowing large quantities of coal to be delivered cheaply.

An illustration of Tottington Print Works in c 1912, showing the printing and engraving rooms, and part of the engine and boiler houses with their associated chimneys

The line proved to be profitable immediately, and was of considerable benefit to the print works. This period coincided with the height of prosperity in the printing industry, providing Samuel Knowles & Company with sufficient profits to expand their works further. By the end of the 1880s, the dye house and a new drying room in the western part of the site, and the bleach croft and print shop to the east, had all been extended over the Kirklees Brook. A new steam engine and several boilers had also been purchased, and a new gas works added to the north-western corner of the site. The Company had also purchased the Kirklees Print Works, situated less than 500m down stream.

In response to the trade depression that beset the printing industry in the following decade, Samuel Knowles & Company amalgamated with the newly formed Calico Printers' Association in 1899. This enabled the continued expansion and investment in the works, despite its age; by 1913, there were 80 print works operating in Lancashire, of which only 16 had been built before 1846.

The 1920s brought a further decline in the industry, and a decision to close Tottington Print Works was enacted in 1927, followed shortly by the demolition of most of the buildings. Since demolition, the abandoned site has become colonised by vegetation and a diverse range of habitats, leading to the designation of the area as a Site of Biological Importance and a Local Nature Reserve. However, the remains of the print works that extend through the woodland on both sides of the Kirklees Brook provide a powerful reminder of the site's rich industrial heritage.

The visible remains of the bleach croft at Tottington Print Works in January 2011

The Kirklees Brook entering the culvert beneath the floor of the dye house

The Archaeological Project

The extensive remains of Tottington Print Works include a stone-built, arched culvert that channels the Kirklees Brook through the site. The culvert was extended as the print works developed, reaching a length in excess of 130m by the early twentieth century, although demolition of the buildings that spanned the brook has reduced the culvert to just one third of its former length.

The brook emerging from the culvert after heavy rainfall

In 2010, in line with a European directive to 'naturalise' watercourses wherever possible, the Environment Agency carried out a feasibility study for removing the culvert, as it impedes the flow of the brook. This study needed to consider any archaeological constraints prior to devising a proposal. Bury Council, as the landowner, was also keen to gain a better understanding of the remains that survive across the rest of the print works' site.

These objectives were met by an archaeological survey of the above-ground remains, coupled with some limited excavation as a community based project under the supervision of OA North. In addition to assessing the extent and heritage value of the remains, it was hoped that the project would help to raise the profile of the site locally, and inform a strategy for the long-term management of the print works.

The above-ground remains of Tottington Print Works are spread across an area of some 62,000 square metres on both sides of the Kirklees Brook. These remains include massive stone-built foundations for steam engines, stone cisterns, dye becks, and extensive fragments of walls, some of which line the channel of the brook as it flows south to its confluence with the Irwell.

The remains of the foundation bed for a steam engine adjacent to the bleach croft

Following the removal of scrub vegetation by members of the British Trust for Conservation Volunteers (BTCV), the extent and survival of buried structures was tested by the limited excavation of two targeted areas. This was carried out by volunteers attending a total of 12 pre-arranged events, including several public open days, over a period of three months.

The first area to be targeted for excavation was on the site of the bleach croft, in the north-eastern part of the print works complex. Whilst this area had become overgrown since the demolition of the building, the tops of several stone cisterns were visible protruding through the vegetation, suggesting that buried remains were likely to survive *in-situ*.

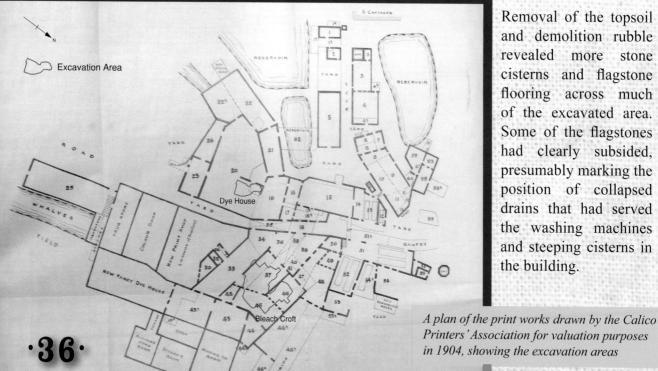

Removal of the topsoil and demolition rubble revealed more stone cisterns and flagstone flooring across much of the excavated area. Some of the flagstones had clearly subsided, presumably marking the position of collapsed drains that had served the washing machines and steeping cisterns in the building.

A plan of the print works drawn by the Calico Printers' Association for valuation purposes in 1904, showing the excavation areas

One of the iron 'cloth bines' set into the floor of the bleach croft

Excavation also revealed the tops of two large iron cisterns. These almost certainly were the remains of the two 'circular wrought-iron cloth bines', 6ft 6in (1.98m) deep, with wooden linings, referred to in an inventory and valuation of the works compiled by the Calico Printers' Association in 1904. Each cistern had a diameter of 2.40m, and had been sunk into the floor of the bleach croft.

A row of three large stone cisterns was discovered in the southern part of the excavated area. These had been set into the floor against the wall of the bleach croft, and are likely to be the steeping cisterns referred to in the inventory of 1904.

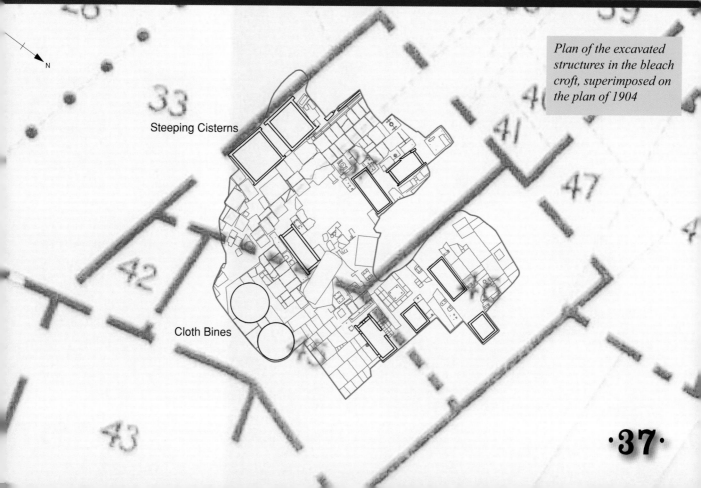

Plan of the excavated structures in the bleach croft, superimposed on the plan of 1904

Steeping Cisterns

Cloth Bines

Possible chemic cistern, with foundation blocks for the machinery

A twentieth-century tight-strand washing machine

Several rectangular stone-built cisterns, all sunk slightly into the floor, were also unearthed. Whilst one of these had been worked from a single block of stone, most comprised four huge slabs, each 6in (0.15m) thick, braced by an iron bar at each end. The cisterns were of various lengths up to 9ft (2.74m), but were uniformly 4ft (1.22m) wide. One of the shorter examples, measuring 7ft (2.13m) long, had stone blocks set at each corner, each retaining metal tie-down bolts for the legs of a machine. It is possible that this was the chemic cistern listed in the inventory of 1904.

The sides of some of the excavated cisterns tapered inwards, producing a V-shaped profile, with a drain hole at their base. Two large examples in the north-western part of the bleach croft had been placed in a 5ft (1.52m) wide stone-lined trough that was set into the floor in this part of the building. This trough and the cisterns may have been associated with washing machines. The upper surfaces of the component slabs were damaged slightly, although two semi-circular cut-outs could be discerned, marking the position of a roller or power shaft.

The second area to be investigated lay within an extension to the dye house that had been built in the second half of the nineteenth century. This had spanned the Kirklees Brook, requiring the culvert to be lengthened. The removal of layers of topsoil and brick rubble uncovered the intact flagstone floor of the dye house, which had been laid over the culvert. The flagstones all varied in size, and had been laid fairly irregularly.

Cistern for washing machine, set in a trough

Volunteers with the Bury Rangers excavating the dye house

The southern part of the excavated area was dominated by the base for a small horizontal steam engine. This was constructed largely from huge stone blocks, although a concrete section had been added at one end in the twentieth century, presumably to allow a larger engine to be installed.

Two stone dye becks were also discovered, although these were not excavated below their upper surface. The becks were set into the floor at the northern end of the dye house, and within the footprint of the early nineteenth-century building.

The foundation base for a horizontal steam engine in the dye house

Many different artefacts were discovered during the excavation. Ceramic objects were the most common, and included fragments of large earthenware bowls and storage jars, typical of a nineteenth-century domestic context. Fragments of finer tablewares, such as transfer-printed plates, cups and saucers, were also found, which had perhaps derived from the manager's office.

Numerous pieces of ceramic 'pot-eyes' were also unearthed. These will have been fitted to machines and set in partition walls, and provided a smooth surface to guide the rope of cloth being winched between different processes in the bleach croft.

Perhaps the most interesting objects from the site, however, have been discovered by chance by members of the local community, and passed on for inclusion with the project archive. These include several tallies that bear the company name, and some tools that would have been used in the works.

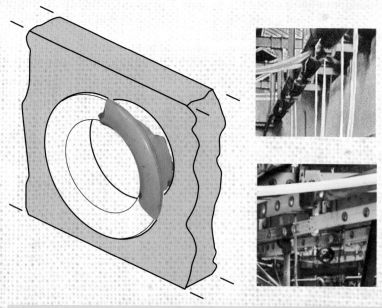

Fragment of a pot-eye recovered from Tottington, showing how it would have been mounted, and other pot-eyes in use

Copper-alloy and aluminium tallies used for 'clocking-in' to work

In total, some 245 square metres of the bleach croft were cleared of scrub vegetation and demolition rubble, and another 40 square metres of overburden were removed from the floor of the dye house. These two areas covered only a fraction of the entire site, and yet the excavation revealed fascinating and well-preserved remains of the print works, and demonstrated the likelihood that buried elements of other parts of the works will survive. Taken together with the extensive above-ground structures and numerous reservoirs that exist, the site of Tottington Print Works is clearly an important heritage asset; the site can be seen to be one of the best remaining examples of a nineteenth-century print works in the county, and makes a key contribution to the historic character and appearance of the Kirklees Valley Local Nature Reserve.

The project also elicited a high level of interest and support from local residents of all ages. Some were keen just to view the site and learn about its history, or share their local knowledge and stories of the print works, whilst others had an appetite to explore its physical remains by joining in the excavation.

Volunteers of all ages excavating the bleach croft

ARCHAEOLOGY AND DEVELOPMENT

This booklet has attempted to explain the historical significance of the printing trade to the region's textile industry, and highlight the value of the surviving remains as heritage assets. Despite the importance and scale of the industry, however, very few print works survive in anything like their original condition, and those buildings that do remain are vulnerable to change and redevelopment.

As with all other branches of the textile industry, printing experienced a significant decline during the second half of the twentieth century, leading ultimately to the closure of most of the works. Some of the print works in the River Irwell catchment area were converted for alternative industrial uses, particularly as bleach works or paper mills, but the decline of these industries has in many cases led to demolition. Printing is still carried on commercially by a few firms in north-west England, although this is on a small scale and usually for niche markets. In most cases, moreover, the printing process has been updated with the application of digital technology, and the works tend to comprise modern buildings, often making the historic structures redundant.

Eden Wood Mill on the Dearden Brook near Ramsbottom was built as a cotton mill in 1801, but was used as a specialised hand-block print works between 1968 and 2001, when the buildings were abandoned

The clearance of disused industrial works is frequently a preferred option for bringing new life to 'brownfield' sites, not least because the retention and refurbishment of the historic buildings is seldom the most cost-effective option for redevelopment. The layout of a typical print works, described in the 1840s as being 'very irregularly built...they seem to be a succession of after-thoughts', can also be disadvantageous to finding new uses, such as conversion for residential purposes. This can be achieved successfully, however, as demonstrated by the impressive conversion of Wallsuches Bleach Works to a prestige housing development.

Set on the edge of the West Pennine Moors overlooking Horwich, Wallsuches developed progressively from the 1770s to form a large textile-finishing works, with integrated bleaching, dyeing and printing departments. Despite having closed in 1933, most of the buildings remained in use as an engineering works and the site has survived as a rare example of a largely intact works. The extensive complex of stone and brick buildings includes a bleach croft, a tall engine house, drying rooms, and several warehouses, cart sheds and stables. The unique and distinctive historic character of the assortment of buildings has been retained during its conversion for residential use between 2000 and 2009, a process that was guided by a long-running programme of archaeological survey and excavation, and advice from GMAU.

Wallsuches Bleach Works was established in 1777 by John and Thomas Ridgway, described as one of the most enterprising bleaching firms of the time. Wallsuches was one of the first works in the country to apply chemical bleaching processes on an industrial scale

The importance of the historic structures at Wallsuches was acknowledged at a national level in 1996 when the buildings were awarded Grade II listed status, becoming the only textile-finishing complex in Greater Manchester to be afforded this degree of statutory protection. The standing remains of other works are less secure, as their historic character may not be sufficiently important for their preservation to outweigh the benefits of a development opportunity. Whilst recognising that change is inevitable, the importance of appropriate management of the historic environment is stressed in current national planning polices that are set out in Planning Policy Statement PPS 5 *Planning for the Historic Environment*. PPS 5 advises that an accurate record should be made of historic structures and buried archaeological remains that are to be damaged by new development. This process is known as 'preservation by record', and it leads to the creation of a technical report and site archive. The appropriate level of recording that is required is considered on a case-by-case basis, and is guided by the professional advice of GMAU.

The basic level of documenting a building or industrial complex is a photographic survey, which provides an effective means of preserving the site by record. One such survey was carried out by UMAU prior to the demolition of several buildings at the Stormer Hill Works. Situated less than 500m upstream of Tottington Print Works, Stormer Hill was established in *c* 1816 as a cotton mill and, like several water-powered mills in the Kirklees Valley, was converted to bleaching in the 1820s. It remained in use as a textile-finishing works until 1997, and was the last of the important group of nineteenth-century works in the Kirklees Valley to close. The comprehensive photographic survey captured the detail of a group of nineteenth-century buildings prior to their demolition, and enabled several phases in their development to be identified.

PPS 5 also advises that an accurate record should be made where buried remains are to be lost to development. This advice was followed by Bury Council whilst considering the proposal to lay the West East Link Main across the Borough, and following consultation with GMAU, attached a condition to the planning consent that required a scheme of archaeological investigation.

Aerial view of Stormer Hill Works taken shortly after its closure in 1997, showing the characteristic components and layout of a textile-finishing works (©GMAU Archive)

The West East Link Main during construction

The programme of works was intended to establish whether any important archaeological remains survived along the pipeline route, and to make an appropriate record of any that were found to exist. The importance of the buried remains found in Springwater Park merited their excavation to ensure that a detailed record was compiled. As is frequently the case with infrastructure projects and development schemes, the archaeological fieldwork for the West East Link Main formed only one element of the construction programme, and the surveys and excavations were carried out to a fixed timetable in a construction-site environment.

The investigation of Tottington Print Works also stemmed from planning obligations, again following advice from GMAU, which in this instance required an assessment of the impact on the heritage value of the site that would arise through deculverting the Kirklees Brook. This requirement was fulfilled in part by local residents working under the guidance of professional archaeologists, whilst the opportunity provided by Bury Council to assess the importance of the historic remains across the wider site brought considerable added value to the project, and enabled a larger number of local residents to engage actively in discovering the archaeology of the site. The closer involvement of local communities and interest groups in excavations led by professional archaeologists is becoming increasingly popular, both within the planning system and as heritage-led projects.

Some special interest groups have also carried out important work, such as a major study that was commenced by members of the Manchester Region Industrial Archaeology Society in 2010. This aims to identify all of the textile-finishing works that had been established in Greater Manchester, and assess the extent of the surviving sites. This project is a good example of an interest group carrying out important research that can inform the planning system, and help to ensure the future management of those surviving elements of historic textile-finishing sites.

GLOSSARY

ALUM: a double salt of aluminium sulphate in combination with either potassium sulphate or ammonium sulphate, used in the textile industry as a mordant.

ANILINE DYE: a synthetic organic compound used to colour fabric. Until the introduction of petrochemicals in the mid-twentieth century, the primary raw material for synthetic dye was obtained from coal tar.

BACKFILLING: the final operation performed on cloth to make it ready for sale was often to impregnate it with a stiffening agent, such as starch. Where this was required on only one side of the cloth, the process was known as backfilling.

BECK: a trough or vat, usually of stone of wood, used in the dyeing process.

BLEACH CROFT: a piece of land or building where bleaching is carried out.

BUCKING an initial stage in the bleaching process, which involved boiling the cloth in alkaline lye.

CALICO a plain-woven textile made from unbleached cotton.

CALENDAR: a series of pressure rollers used to form or smooth a sheet of material.

CHEMIC: bleaching-powder solution.

DASH WHEEL: large hollow wheels divided into compartments, which were filled with bundles of cloth and water. Impurities were washed out of the cloth as the dash wheel was spun rapidly. Dash wheels were superseded by an improved type of washing machine invented in 1828 by David Bentley.

✳ FUSTIAN: strong, twilled cloth, with a linen warp and a cotton weft, although the term is also used to describe a variety of heavy woven cloth prepared for menswear. The production of fustian increased steadily in the Manchester area during the early seventeenth century.

✳ INDIGO: a plant native to India and other Asian countries, which creates a blue dye.

✳ KIER: a large cylindrical boiler or vat used in bleaching or scouring cotton cloth.

✳ LODGE: another name for a reservoir.

✳ LOGWOOD: a species of flowering tree of the legume family, logwood is native to southern Mexico and northern Central America, and was an important natural source of dye.

✳ LYE: a corrosive alkaline substance, commonly sodium hydroxide (also known as caustic soda) or potassium hydroxide, used for dissolving sticky substances such as fat.

✳ MADDER: a red dye from the roots of the madder plant, imported mainly from the Middle East.

✳ MANGLE: a machine consisting of two or more rollers used to wring water from wet cloth.

✳ MORDANT: a substance used to fix dyes to fabrics.

✳ STENTER: a machine used to stretch and straighten bleached cloth in preparation for printing certain formal styles of pattern.

FURTHER READING

Aspin, C, 1995 *The First Industrial Society: Lancashire, 1750 – 1850*, Preston

Barfoot, JR, 1840 *The Progress of Cotton*, London

Grindon, LH, 1882 *Lancashire: Brief Historical and Descriptive Notes*, London

Harvey, C, and Press, J, 1991 *William Morris: Design and Enterprise in Victorian Britain*, Manchester

McNeil, R, and Nevell, M, 2000 *A Guide to the Industrial Archaeology of Greater Manchester*, Manchester

Miller, I, and Gregory, R, 2010 *The Rock Triangle, Bury: The Archaeology of an Industrial Suburb*, Greater Manchester's Past Revealed, **3**, Lancaster

Nevell, M (ed), 2003 *From Farmer to Factory Owner: Models, Methodology and Industrialisation*, Manchester

Turnbull, JG, 1951 *A History of Calico Printing in Great Britain*, Altrincham

A copy of each of the detailed excavation reports has been deposited with the GMAU Archive.

Other books in the *Greater Manchester's Past Revealed* series:

(available from Oxford Archaeology North, Mill 3, Moor Lane Mills, Moor Lane, Lancaster, LA1 1GF)

Piccadilly Place: Uncovering Manchester's Industrial Origins – **1**

The Rock Triangle, Bury: The Archaeology of an Industrial Suburb – **2**

Discovering Coccium: The Archaeology of Roman Wigan – **3**

Rediscovering Bradford: archaeology in the Engine Room of Manchester – **4**

Slices Through Time: Greater Manchester's Historic Character Revealed – **5**